Printed and Published by D. C. THOMSON & CO., LTD., 185 Fleet Street, London EC4A 2HS.
© D. C. THOMSON & CO., LTD., 2000.
ISBN 0 85116 743 8

THE MENACE MINDER!

JUST A SECOND, WALTER!

SKIP

D-DON'T M·MENACE ME, P. PLEASE!

I'M NOT GOING TO MENACE YOU...

... I'M GOING TO STOP YOU CATCHING COLD! I'M PROTECTING YOU!

B·BUT IT'S THE MIDDLE OF SUMMER!

CAN'T TAKE CHANCES— YOU KNOW WHAT SUMMER'S LIKE!

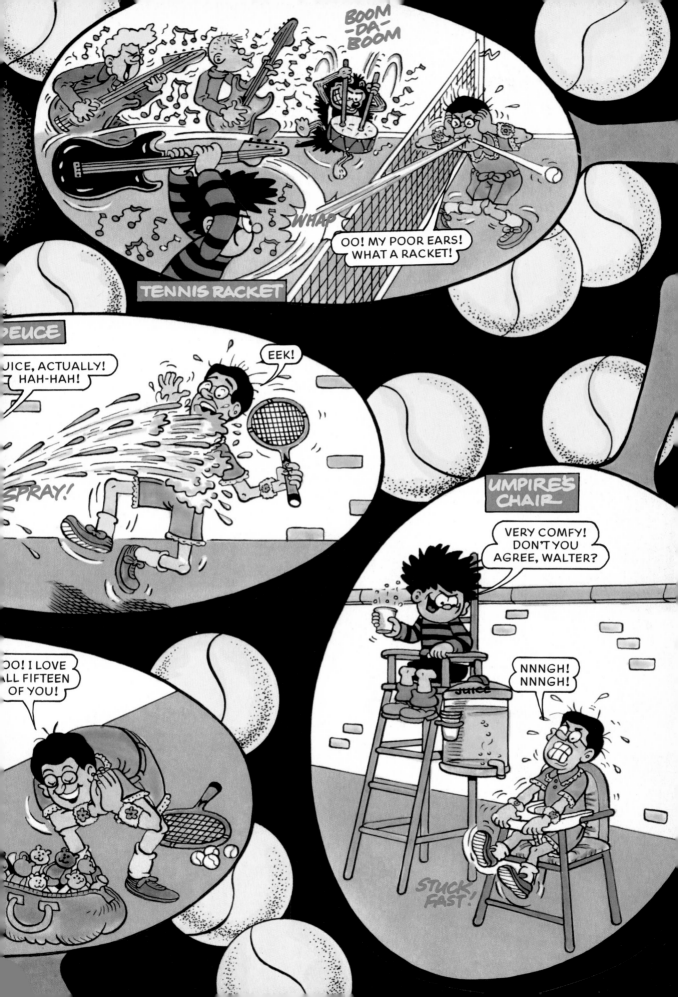

DENNIS and GNASHER are—
OUT OF THEIR TREE!

WAHEY! HIYA, READERS.

GNOO-HOO!

OUR TREE HOUSE IS BRILLIANT — BUT IT NEEDS A FEW RUNNING REPAIRS.

GNYEAH!

SNAP!

SNAP!

HANDS UP!

THIS IS THE ONLY WAY I CAN GET THIS JERSEY OFF HIM TO BE WASHED!

SNATCH

B-BUT, MUM...

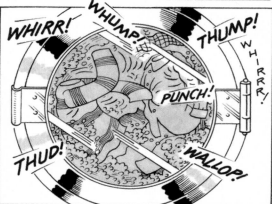

WHIRR! WHUMP! THUMP! WHIRR! PUNCH! THUD! WALLOP!

THEN—

WAH!

YOU SHOULDN'T HAVE PUT MY JERSEY IN WITH THAT SOFT STUFF, MUM!

SHORTLY— MY JERSEY AND I ARE PLAYING FOOTBALL!

OH, NO! BALL BOY'S SURE TO SCORE, UNLESS....

PHEEP!

EH?

PUSH

EH? GOAL!

THUD!

ERK!

READER'S VOICE

GASP! THAT'S SOME JERSEY, DENNIS!

IT SURE IS, READER....

....BUT GNASHER'S ALSO SOME DOG!

BAH!

HEH-HEH! I WAS HAVING A GNAP UNDER THAT WARM JERSEY!

HEH! HEH!

ZOOM!

GNASHER'S BIG CAT SAFARI
1 THE LEOPARD
GNEE HEE-HEE!
GET OFF MY BACK, MAN!

HISTORY MYSTERY!

HISTORY NEXT...

OH, BOY!

... STARTING WITH CAPTAIN TEACH, ALIAS "BLACKBEARD"!

BLACKBEARD

THIS HISTORY'S ALL ABOUT PIRATES SWASHING THEIR BUCKLES AND THINGS—SO ZIP YOUR LIP, READER!

SNIFF! VERY SORRY, I'M SURE!
READER'S VOICE

BACK HOME—

SHE'S ALMOST READY TO LAUNCH, GNASHER! YO-HO-HO AND A BOTTLE OF RASPBERRY FIZZY POP!

HAMMER! SAW! BANG! THUD!

Dennis's shed

CAPTAIN BLACKHAIR, THE SCOURGE OF THE SEVEN STREETS, SETS SAIL! STEADY AS SHE GOES, FIRST MATE GNASHER!

ZOOM!

THE MENACE'S APPRENTICE

I WANT YOU TO KEEP YOUR YOUNG COUSIN HAPPY FOR A WHILE, DENNIS.

MY HERO!

SIGH! OK, DAD!

I'M GOING TO SCARE PEOPLE WITH MY MASK!

GREAT! AN APPRENTICE MENACE!

SO—

BOO!

GIGGLE!

WHAT A SHAME! EVEN THE PRINCE OF SOFTIES IS LAUGHING AT MY COUSIN!

RECKON I'LL JUST HAVE TO GIVE MY KID COUSIN A HELPING HAND!

PEAS

WATER

Dennis's shed

SOON—

BOO!

DON'T MAKE ME...

...F-FAINT!

I DID IT! I SCARED HIM!

JUST DO MY GOOD DEED AND WAKEN BERTIE UP.

SQUIRT!

HERE COMES SOFTY WALTER, BUT IF I SCARE HIM, HE'LL JUST LAUGH AT ME AGAIN.

NO, HE WON'T...

...NOT WITH THIS WORM DOWN HIS NECK!

BOO!

HA-HA...

...ARGH!

PLOP!

HE'S SCARED TOO—I'M A REAL MENACE NOW!

WAH!

LATER—

I'VE HAD NOTHING BUT COMPLAINTS ABOUT YOU! YOU'RE GOING TO BE...

ERK!

WAIT!

READER'S VOICE—

DENNIS WAS ONLY KEEPING HIS YOUNG COUSIN HAPPY—HONESTLY!

READER'S VOICE

HE WAS?

SO—

GROAN! I'M BEING SENT EARLY TO BED...

...WITH MY SUPPER! YIPPEEYAHOO!

WELL, I DIDN'T KNOW WHETHER TO PUNISH HIM OR REWARD HIM, READERS!

THE NORMAN CONQUEST PART 1

HUMANS ARE DISGUSTING EATERS.

Look—

CHOMP!

SQUIRT!

SPLAT!

I'LL SHOW THEM THE CORRECT WAY TO EAT A JAM DOUGHNUT.

FIRST GET INTO POSITION . . .

SNIFF!

SNIFF!

. . . AND SUCK IT ON TO YOUR SNOUT.

SUCK!

THEN PUNCTURE WITH A TUSK.

PRANG

AND SUCK THE JAM OUT.

SUCK!

REMOVE THE SUGAR FROM THE OUTSIDE . . .

. . . THEN EAT. CHOMP.

CHOMP!

MUST TRY THIS! TWO MORE JAM DOUGHNUTS, WAITER.

BEFORE TRYING THIS, READERS, DO ONE IMPORTANT THING . . .

SHAKE !

MUMFLE! WHAT A MESS.

YUCK!

. . . MAKE SURE YOU'RE A PIG.

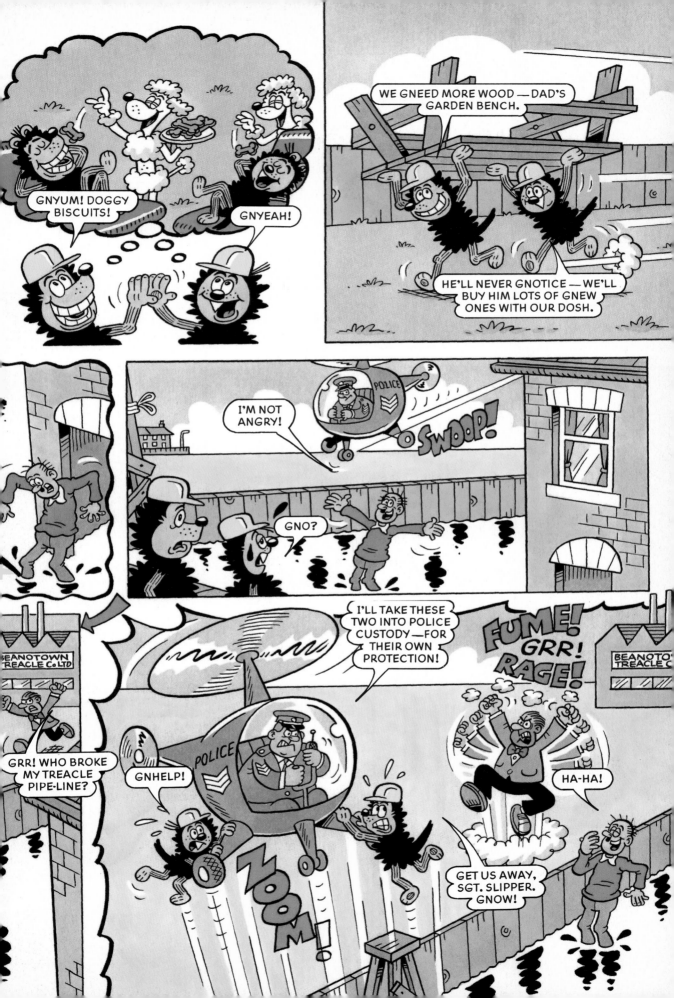

GNASHER'S
BIG CAT
SAFARI
2 THE CHEETAH
GNEE-OW-AH! ME TARZAN, YOU CHEETAH!
CHEETAH WAS A CHIMP, YOU TWERP!

GNIPPER? HE'S GNUTS!

RIGHT! I'M GOING TO PROVE TO THE MENACE THAT I'M THE BAD LAD IN THE DENNIS BOOK — ME, NASTY NORMAN!

I CHALLENGE YOU TO THE MENACE TEST!

EH?

HAR-HAR! WHAT'S YOUR ANSWER?

I ACCEPT!

DOOF!

WHAP!

GNOORAY!

THE **NORMAN** CONQUEST

LET SLEEPING MENACES LIE!

TIME TO GET UP, DENNIS!

ZZZZZ!

SAME THING EVERY MORNING— I'VE GOT TO WAKEN UP THIS SLEEPY-HEAD!

ZZZZ!

SNIGGER!

ZZZZZ!

AND AN ICE-COLD SHOWER IS THE ONLY WAY TO DO IT!

WAH! BRRRR!

CRIMEWATCH O.K.?

IN THE POLICE STATION—

PAY ATTENTION, NEW RECRUITS—I'LL TELL YOU WHAT TO EXPECT ON YOUR FIRST DAY.

THIS IS WALTER, PRINCE OF SOFTIES—YOU'LL HAVE NO BOTHER WITH HIM...

...KEEP YOUR EYE ON THIS ONE, THOUGH—THIS IS THE MENACE! AND REMEMBER, LADS—BE CAREFUL OUT THERE!

ERK!

SOON—

EVER HAD THE FEELING YOU WERE BEING WATCHED?

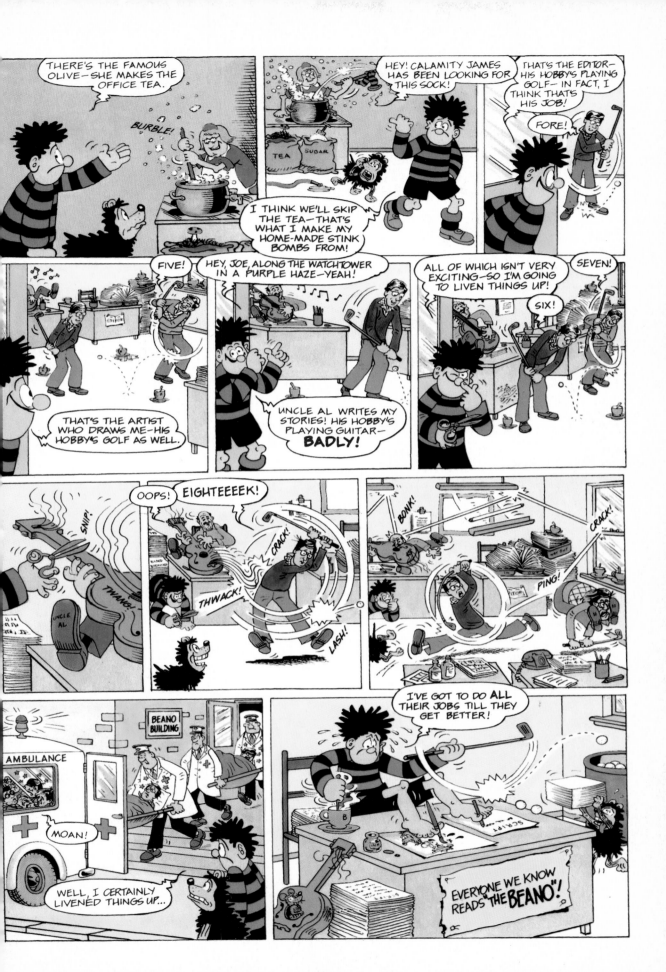

ARE YOU THE GREAT SGT. SLIPPER?

WHIRR!

SGT. SLIPPER OF THE YARD

GLORY DAYS. BUT THEN I WAS TRANSFERRED TO BEANOTOWN.

HELP US!

PLEASE!

GO ON!

WHIRR!

OF COURSE, WITH MY POLICE SKILLS AND SHARP BRAIN, I SOON WORKED OUT WHO THE PROBLEM-MAKERS WERE!

THEM!

WANTED

WHIRR!

— ALAS!

FZZT!

POLICE

BOOM!

SPLAT!

CUSTARD FLAN

YOU SEE, IT WASN'T REALLY GNASHER.

YOU GREAT BLITHERING TWIT! I'M UNDERCOVER, TRYING TO CATCH THE MENACES!

CHIEF CONSTABLE IN GNASHER COSTUME

OH, MY!

N

LOOK OUT, LONDON!

The Menace family are sight-seeing in London.

SIGHT-SEEING
Tour of
LONDON

SEE:
THE DOME
ST PAUL'S
HER MAJES
GAFF
BIG BEN
SMALL FRED
TINY TIMMY

COR! THIS BUS IS OPEN-TOPPED. JUST THE KIND THE CUP WINNERS SHOW OFF THE CUP WITH!

WE WON THE CUP! WE WON THE CUP!

Bea's Potty contents: Best Not ask!

EH?

THINK THE STATUE IS TOO TALL?

SAY 'CHEESY FEET'!

NO WAY — JUST RIGHT!

WHAT'S THE TOP SPEED?

QUITE QUICK, ACTUALLY!

WAHEY!

NIGEL PARKINSON

DON'T WORRY, MENACE PARENTS. I KNOW WHERE TO TAKE THEM NOW!

OH, YES, WELL, ER . . .

JUST BIG ENOUGH FOR A DOUBLE-DECKER

THIS DOESN'T LOOK LIKE A TOURIST ATTRACTION.

GNUH? LIKE A GARAGE!

CLOSE ALL WINDOWS

IN

AARGH! WORSE!

'WOOD' YOU BELIEVE IT?

OUR LAST BIT OF COAL, NO MORE FUEL IN THE HOUSE AND THE COALMAN DOESN'T DELIVER UNTIL TOMORROW.

GO AND GET SOME FIREWOOD, DENNIS.

RIGHT, MUM!

BUT—

THE FIREWOOD'S ALL SOLD, BUT YOU CAN HAVE THAT OLD TREE—IF YOU CAN TAKE IT AWAY! HEH-HEH!

TIMBER MERCHANTS

SOLD OUT

HMM!

A MENACE IS NEVER STUCK.

SPREAD!

MEAT PASTE

TOPPLE!

CHOMP!

YUMMY! GNASH!

A. LOG. FIREWOOD

TIMBER MERCHANTS

SOLD OUT

GO TO IT, DOGS— TIMBER!

HAIR TODAY - GONE TODAY!

FUNNY! I DIDN'T ORDER A NEW BLACK CARPET.

EEK!

IT'S NOT A CARPET— GNASHER'S BEEN MOULTING.

GNERK! MY FANS WON'T RECOGNISE ME.